Published in 2021 by Hardie Grant Explore,
an imprint of Hardie Grant Publishing

Hardie Grant Explore (Melbourne)
Wurundjeri Country
Building 1, 658 Church Street
Richmond, Victoria 3121

Hardie Grant Explore (Sydney)
Gadigal Country
Level 7, 45 Jones Street
Ultimo, NSW 2007

www.hardiegrant.com/au/explore

A catalogue record for this
book is available from the
National Library of Australia

Hardie Grant acknowledges the Traditional Owners of
the Country on which we work, the Wurundjeri people
of the Kulin Nation and the Gadigal people of the
Eora Nation, and recognises their continuing connection
to the land, waters and culture. We pay our respects to
their Elders past and present.

The First Scientists
ISBN 9781741177527

10 9 8 7 6 5 4

Publisher Melissa Kayser
Project editor Rachel Rawling
Editor Irma Gold
Proofreader Marly Wells
Design Keisha Leon
Typesetting Hannah Schubert
Science consultant Anika Mostaert

Colour reproduction by Splitting Image Colour Studio

Printed in China by 1010 Printing International Limited

THE FIRST SCIENTISTS

COREY TUTT

Illustrations by Blak Douglas

Hardie Grant

EXPLORE

THE AIATSIS MAP OF INDIGENOUS AUSTRALIA

This map attempts to represent the language, social or nation groups of Aboriginal Australia. It shows only the general locations of larger groupings of people which may include clans, dialects or individual languages in a group. It used published resources from the eighteenth century-1994 and is not intended to be exact, nor the boundaries fixed. It is not suitable for native title or other land claims. David R Horton (creator), © AIATSIS, 1996. No reproduction without permission. To purchase a print version visit: https://shop.aiatsis.gov.au/

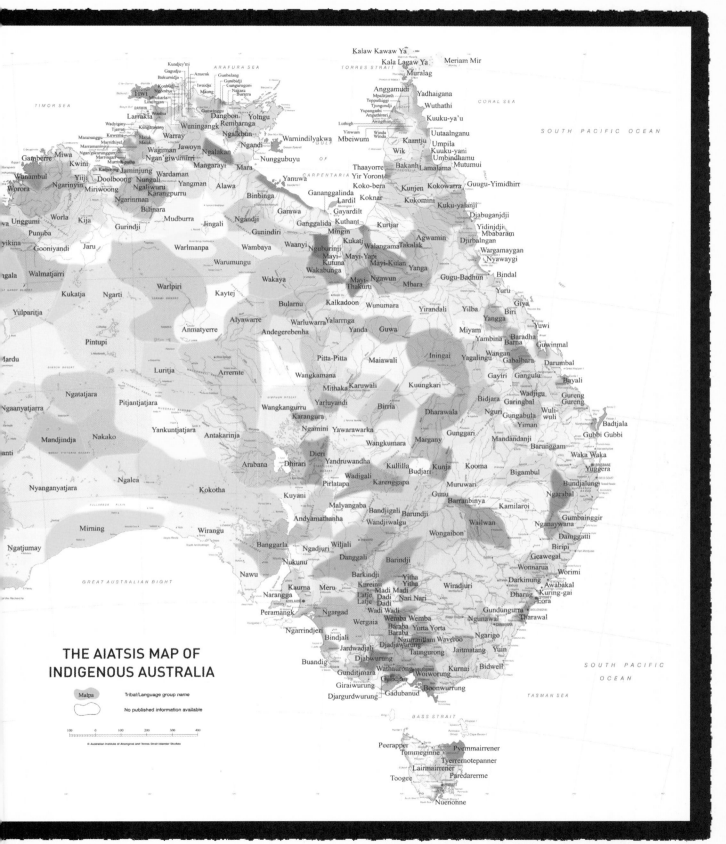

THE AIATSIS MAP OF
INDIGENOUS AUSTRALIA

Malpa — Tribal/Language group name

No published information available

© Australian Institute of Aboriginal and Torres Strait Islander Studies

Hi, I'm Corey. I'm a proud Kamilaroi man and I love all things science!

Today we have many First Nations scientists who are leading the way. Our people have much knowledge and experience to share.

To all the deadly junior scientists out there, you too can be like the first scientists, observing and discovering the answers to life's questions. And maybe one day you'll work as a scientist, sharing your knowledge.

While reading this book, take notice of the small things around you. Are the birds chirping in a particular way? Which flowers are blossoming? What stars can you see? This is all science, and science is all around us.

Don't be scared to ask the questions *why* and *how*? Challenge the narrative, and create your own.

CONTENTS

THE FIRST ASTRONOMERS

The first scientists across the land looked to the skies. They asked questions and found answers there. Whether it was finding food or predicting the weather, the stars and the sky played an important role in culture and how we understood and continue to understand the world.

Today, over 500 different nations and clans in Australia still maintain a relationship with the sky. We look to the skies as a familiar friend. There we find answers to the same questions the first scientists asked.

In the eastern states of Australia, the First Nations people have an incredible way of reading the stories of the stars, and applying it to everyday life.

EMU IN THE SKY

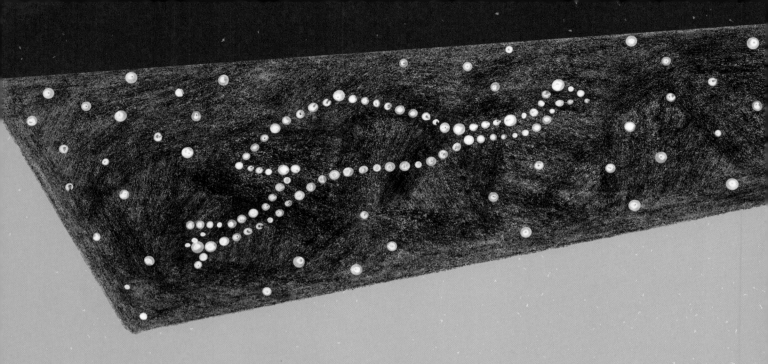

The Emu in the Sky (or Dark Emu) is a dark constellation that forms the shape of an emu. With lighter constellations you trace the stars to form a shape and a story, but with the Dark Emu it's different. Instead you trace the dark patches between the stars to find the Emu.

Can you spot the Emu in the Sky? Look south to the constellation known as the Southern Cross. You will see the Coalsack Nebula, the dark patch near the bottom towards the left. This is the Emu's head. The neck and body are formed by dark patches that stretch across the Milky Way. Together they form the outline of an emu.

The first astronomers of Kamilaroi Country, my people, look to Gawarrgay (our name for the Dark Emu) for guidance. Elders teach us to look at the position of the Emu after the sun goes down to tell the seasons and predict when it is time to collect emu eggs for food.

In April and May, Gawarrgay starts to rise. This is when emus are laying eggs. If Gawarrgay looks like it is sitting down, roosting on a nest, we know the birds are sitting on their eggs. This happens in June and July.

In August and September, Kamilaroi people see Gawarrgay facing down in the sky. This tells us that the chicks are hatching, and it's time to hold special ceremonies. In October and November, as the weather heats up emus sit in waterholes to cool off. When it looks like water is spilling out of the holes of the Dark Emu and falling from the sky, my people know that seasonal rain is on its way.

In a similar way, Yamaji people look for Nyarluwarri (the Seven Sisters, or Pleiades star cluster). In April, when they see the stars low on the horizon after the sun sets, they know that emu eggs are ready for harvesting. They are highly nutritious. Did you know that an emu egg contains the equivalent nutrition of 10 chicken eggs? Great for deadly bodybuilders!

You can see a Dark Emu engraving in Ku-ring-gai Chase National Park in Sydney, New South Wales. The Emu in the Sky knowledge is still passed on to new generations. Maybe on a clear night you might look up to the sky and see the Dark Emu and wonder about our first astronomers.

TIME TO HARVEST

The sky held answers to the questions on when to harvest food.

Other nations across Australia use the stars as a guide for hunting. The people in Pitjantjatjara Country use the Seven Sisters star cluster (the Pleiades) to predict when the winter frosts will begin, and to understand the behaviour of animals. When the cluster of stars rises at dawn in June, dingoes begin having their pups.

The Boorong people know that when the star Marpeankurruk (Arcturus) is visible high in the night sky in August, the larvae of the wood ant can be found under logs and stones. These larvae are high in protein and can survive harsh droughts. It is eaten both cooked and raw until September, when the star sets at dusk.

When gardens are planted, the first scientists read the stars to predict the right time to harvest the food.

The Yolŋu people observe a bright red star called Arcturus as a sign that it is time to collect räkay (spike rush). This plant can be used to make baskets and fish traps. It's also a food source. How deadly is that! Räkay is full of carbohydrates, which help produce energy and are part of a healthy diet. The root of the räkay can be eaten raw or roasted. It's also a favourite food for the magpie goose.

In the Torres Strait, Islanders plant yams each year. Yams are like sweet potatoes, and when the 'yam star' rises at dawn, the Islanders know that it's time to harvest them. This happens in late March, towards the end of the kuki (wet season).

The yam star is called Kek in the Kalau Lagau Ya language. It is the star astronomers call Achernar. When the Islanders see it, they know the sager (dry season) is coming, so they hold a special ceremony.

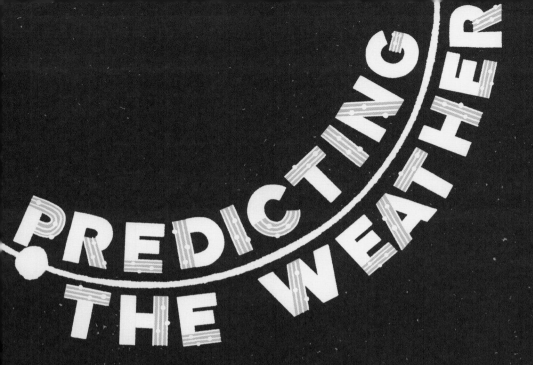

PREDICTING THE WEATHER

Have you ever noticed the stars twinkling? Did you know that the first scientists looked carefully at how they twinkled to predict weather?

Meriam Elders in the eastern Torres Strait teach us to read how the stars blink, twinkle and dance. They call the twinkling stars 'naskasisreda'. The first astronomers long ago figured out that the twinkling stars are caused by wind.

The twinkling stars can tell us that the change of seasons is occurring – from hot to cold, and wet to dry. Late in the year, when the Meriam people see the stars twinkle fast in the sky, they know that the nay gay (hot muggy season) will turn to the kuki (wet season). This is when the trade winds shift from the southeast to the northwest, making the stars blink!

The Wiradjuri people used the sky to predict rainfall along the banks of the Murrumbidgee River. They prepared to move to higher ground as the river became full. Water from rainfall filled the river, causing the surrounding plains to flood.

This told them it was time to move as animals and plants flourish with the flood water. This meant more food!

The Yolŋu people still use the phases of the moon to predict tides. This helps them know if the conditions are good for fishing. The tides are highest at the full and new moon, when we can see all of the moon, or none of it. The tides are calmest when the moon is only half lit, in the first and last quarter.

The Meriam people in the Torres Strait say the best time to fish is when the meb (moon) is in the first or last quarter phases. This is because the tides do not churn up the water as much, making the fish easier to see.

If the moon is a crescent, look at the points on either end. These are called 'cusps'. Meriam people say that when the cusps are pointing straight up (meb metalug em), the moon looks like a bowl collecting water. None of it is reaching the ground, so this is the dry season. When the crescent moon is tilted on its side (meb uag em), it pours the water out, like the rain falling in the kuki (wet season)!

The stars look down on Country and can see all. They looked after the people who first cared for the land, and continue to do so. But did you also know that we all have a little bit of stardust in us? So, the next time someone says you're a superstar, you'd better believe it!

You may have been taught that the first scientists were just hunter-gatherers, but in fact they were some of the greatest minds of their time.

Across Australia there is evidence of tools and engineering feats that are as old as time. Some of them are still used today, from boomerangs and the ever-effective fish traps, while some are the basis for modern materials like bioplastics.

Tools and weapons were carefully designed and refined to work the land to the first scientists's advantage. Today, we have many technological advances, but the voices and designs of the first engineers still remain, and are passed on from generation to generation.

BOOMERANGS

Boomerangs are a commonly known tool of the first scientists. These weapons have to be carefully moulded and cut, and then crafted to be aerodynamic. The rounded edges and wide surface area of a boomerang mean it can glide through the air with ease, hitting its target with force.

Today, this design has been copied and adapted for aeroplane wings. The first scientists were most likely the first peoples to design tools with aerodynamics in mind. So deadly!

FISH TRAPS

NGEMBA
WAILWAN
PEOPLE

The Ngemba Wailwan people have the oldest known fish traps in the world, but most nations used some form of fish traps.

At 40,000 years old they are possibly the oldest human construction still in existence. According to the Dreamtime stories, the great ancestral being Baiame created the fish traps after throwing his net across the Barwon River. His sons then collected the stones and set them up. The Ngemba people call the trap Baiame's Ngunnhu.

The first scientists worked hard to engineer traps so that when the water flowed down the river in a stream, trenches and perfectly placed rocks caused the stream to gradually become shallower and shallower. This left rocks exposed and created holding pens, or enclosed ponds, that were waist-deep, trapping eels, fish and even turtles. These ponds were often tear-shaped and allowed the first scientists to release the animals they didn't need, so that they could be enjoyed by future generations.

Over 20 nations – including Kamilaroi, Morowari, Parrkinji, Weilwan, Barabinja and Ualarai – used these traps. They were a greeting point for clans, and a place to catch and share fish and tools. It was like the original eBay for scientists!

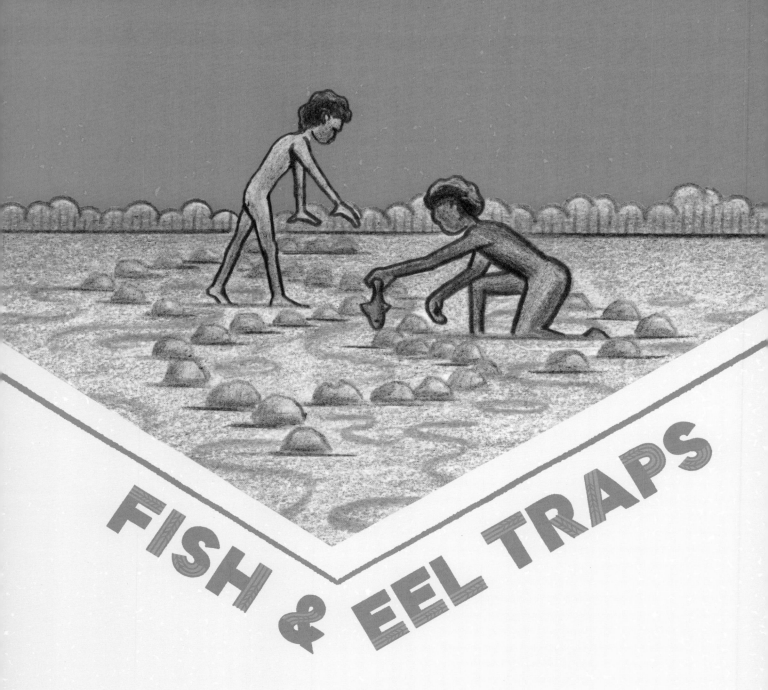

FISH & EEL TRAPS

At least 6,600 years ago, the people of the Gunditjmara Nation in Budj Bim developed complex fish traps.

GUNDITJMARA NATION

These traps were made from a vast network of stone canals and dams to direct and manipulate water levels in nearby creeks as the water level went up, and then down. This then forced fish and other aquatic animals into shallow pools of water where they remained trapped because the water level was too low for them to swim out again. The first engineers released the animals they didn't need. Those they kept were used as food or traded with other nations.

Because of the evidence of these scientific practices, Budj Bim is now a World Heritage site. This means it will be protected for years to come, for future scientists to learn from.

Eels are tricky animals as they can survive out of water for quite a long time, and are also clever climbers, which means they could climb out of the shallow holding pools and escape. To address this problem the Gunditjmara people pioneered a second type of system. They wove grasses together to make a tube-like net. Eels feel safe in dark places and so they would swim into these nets, and then find themselves trapped. The Gunditjmara people would then remove the eels for eating.

The Gadigal people of the Dharug, Dharawal and Darkingjung nations engineered equipment to catch fish in what is now known as the Sydney Basin.

Shellfish were collected and ground down using grinding stones. The shells were cut and moulded into curved, hook-shaped pieces which were smoothed out to become sharp. The patterns on the shellfish hooks made an intriguing lure for the unsuspecting fish – the bright colours mixed with the shiny, smooth, pearly surface made the hook irresistible. Barbs were removed from the shellfish hooks so the fish could be easily caught without causing lasting damage. Fish that weren't needed were then released to fight another day.

DHARUG,
DHARAWAL &
DARKINGJUNG
NATIONS

SHELLFISH TRAPS

YIDINJI PEOPLE

KULIN NATION

GLUE

Did you know that the first scientists invented what we now know as glue? Yes, glue! But we call it resin.

In the desert the Anangu people use resin to bind tools together to make them stronger or more practical. To create the glue, they use the sticky sap from spinifex grass. They heat the base of the grass over a fire and then allow it to cool down naturally. This turns the base into a liquid superglue-like substance which they call kiti.

The Yidinji people make their own resin by mixing parts of the grass tree with the wax from native bees, sand and ash. This creates a cement-like substance that can be used to create structures like huts and fish traps, or to glue sharp arrows onto spears and tools, which are then used for hunting and building.

Resin is also used to waterproof bowls. The people of the Kulin Nation make containers from bark to carry water, and seal the outside with resin. To create strong handles, they use the softer inner layer of bark. It is twisted and tied to create rope, which is then sealed with resin. These bucket-like water containers are called tarnuks.

Today, scientists are learning from the first engineers to create friendly plastics and glues. The University of Queensland has been working with Traditional Owners to create renewable, sustainable materials from spinifex grass. This is important. As we deal with the effects of climate change, we need to find better ways to look after our planet. Plastics never completely break down, and if we can create more sustainable and biodegradable plastics it means less ends up undecomposed in our oceans and in landfill.

SPEARHEADS & ARROWHEADS

For the first engineers every problem had a solution that was developed through careful observation and skill. On Country, the animals were more nimble, faster and stronger than the first engineers. So how could people hunt animals effectively?

JIRRBAL & DYIRBAL PEOPLES

The first engineers modified stone cuts and then moulded them into sharp spearheads that were then attached to large sticks. These sticks were sanded to a smooth finish to allow the spear to glide through the air with ease. This tool made a handy match for the fast kangaroos and wallabies that fed the mob.

But once you've hunted the animal, how do you prepare it for a feast for the mob? The answer is stone tools. These were made from pieces of stone that were cut and sharpened to cut the animals' flesh. It was similar to how today's butchers use a set of knives to carefully cut meat.

Another cool invention is the four-pronged wooden spear from the Jirrbal and Dyirbal people, which was perfect for hunting yummy crabs and fish. The four prongs were extremely sharp and were carefully designed to increase the chance of a fatal shot.

ROPES & HANDLES

Carrying heavy tools by hand could be awkward and difficult, so bark from trees and long grasses were harvested and woven together to form rope. This was then tied to water pouches and tools, adding strength to the tools and offering support.

MILEWA
PEOPLE

CANOES

The first engineers who lived along the Milewa or Tongala, known today as the Murray River, built canoes using large pieces of bark cut from gum trees. The pieces were then warmed over the fire so that the bark softened and curled up. These then formed the sides of the canoe. These two pieces of bark were then joined together with tightly knotted rope, to prevent the canoe from splitting apart. Resin was then applied to seal the canoe and to make it watertight. Sometimes beams were added to keep the sides apart. This knowledge was shared across many of the river nations.

Today, we make canoes out of fibreglass but they are not dissimilar to the designs used by the first engineers all those years ago.

Across the nations there were different ways of grinding down millet and other plants to create flour for bread.

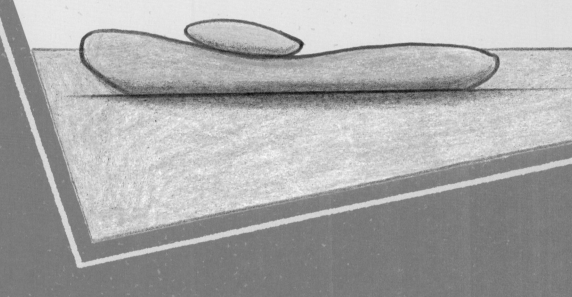

GRINDING STONES

Grinding plates were also used to sharpen tools like arrowheads and spears. Grinding plates have been found across Australia, with some being at least 65,000 years old. The world's earliest grindstones!

Grinding stones were reused for many years. This is an original sustainability practice. How deadly is that!

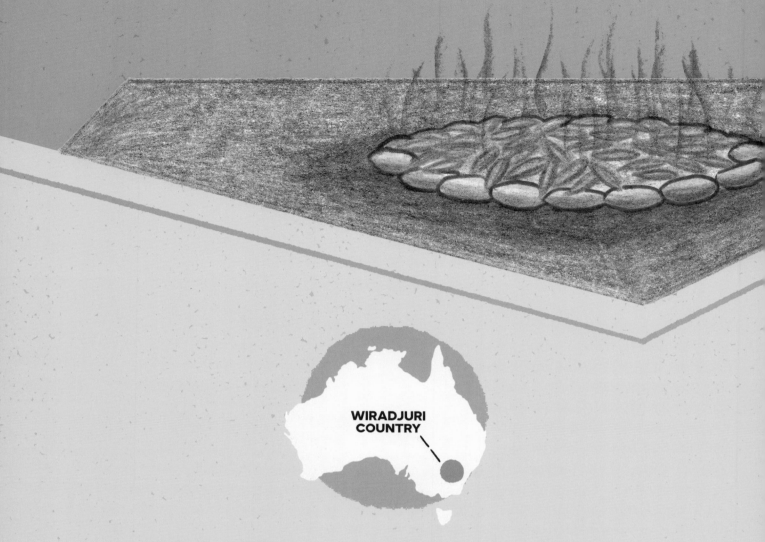

WIRADJURI COUNTRY

BUSH OVENS

The first scientists were expert chefs who engineered extremely clever ways to prepare and cook food. The bush oven is one example.

Wiradjuri Country is a big place and different clans within the Country use many forms of engineering design with subtle differences. One way that the Wiradjuri people make bush ovens is by digging a hole in the ground. Pieces of clay are carefully removed from the ground and rolled into smooth balls. A fire is set. The clay is placed in the fire and once the clay becomes hot, it is carefully removed from the fire with sticks. Then it's placed in a freshly dug hole and quickly covered in leaves. A possum or kangaroo is placed on top of the clay to slowly cook. When the meal is ready, the clay is removed and set aside for reuse another time. This oven is deadly!

The first scientists are the first known people to have created bread, at least 36,000 years ago. The world's first bakers! They used flat rocks to crush and grind kangaroo grass, spinifex and millet that they had harvested. This was then combined with water and moulded into what we now call damper, or johnnycakes.

Bread needs to be cooked slowly because it burns fast. So it was placed in the ashes of the fire and removed after a few hours. This method was also used to cook monitor lizards and snakes because their meat burns quicker than other meats, so it also needed to be cooked slowly. Vegetables and plants were cooked in bush ovens and added to meals. A deadly feast fit for a mob!

DAVID UNAIPON

You may not have heard of the great inventor and writer David Unaipon but if you've ever seen a $50 note you would have laid eyes on Australia's answer to Leonardo da Vinci.

Uncle David Unaipon spent his career dreaming of ideas and inventing. One of these incredible ideas was a handpiece for sheep shearing in 1909. Unaipon's invention made shearing faster and easier than ever before, and became the standard used in modern shears today.

Just like Leonardo da Vinci, Unaipon wanted to fly, and created helicopter designs based on the movement of the boomerang. This was decades before the first helicopter took flight. He also had plans for a perpetual motion machine which he was still developing at the tender age of 79!

As well as being an inventor, Unaipon wrote books and papers. He was the first ever First Nations person to become a published author with his book *Myths and Legends of the Australian Aborigines*. In the following years, Unaipon wrote about, and was vocal for, First Nations rights in Australia.

David Unaipon is an inspiration to all Australians and was one of the deadliest scientists in recent history. Next time you see a $50 dollar note, look at Unaipon and be inspired. Maybe you'll come up with your own big invention or idea!

THE FIRST FORENSIC SCIENTISTS

The first scientists not only cared for Country but they also had the ability to notice small changes in the landscape. It's this attention to detail that has served First Nations peoples for over 65,000 years. In modern times this expertise has often been called on by law enforcement and governments to help find people or animals lost in the bush.

While it's not quite the forensic science you see in spy movies, you'll soon discover how deadly the first forensic scientists are, and how their knowledge is still used today to protect some of our amazing animals.

BUSH TRACKERS

Sometimes when people become lost in the bush the local rescuers will enlist the help of First Nations people. They notice small changes that others miss, like footprints in the sand, or dirt shifted in a certain way, or even different smells.

These trackers were heroes who saved many people who became lost. In August 1864 on Wimmera Country, two Whadjuk people were employed as bush trackers to find the Duff kids – Isaac Cooper (aged 9), Jane Cooper (aged 7) and Frank Duff (aged 3) who were lost in the bush for nine winter days. This was well before the days of GPS and emergency beacons.

WIMMERA
COUNTRY

BUSHRANGERS

The first forensic scientists were responsible for apprehending some of Australia's most notorious criminals. Trackers were employed by police forces across Australia to track and capture bushrangers.

In Argyle Country, trackers were hired to find the infamous Clarke brothers. From 1866, they were wanted for the theft of gold and the suspected murder of four police officers in the Dharawal Nation. The Clarke brothers had spent 18 months terrorising local communities until their capture in 1867 on Walbanga Country.

The Clarke brothers were two of the most dangerous bushrangers of their time. Wiradjuri man Sergeant Major Watkin Wynne, along with fellow Wiradjuri man Tommy Lawson, played a huge role in tracking the Clarke brothers and arresting them. Unfortunately the capture didn't go smoothly and Sergeant Wynne was wounded. Luckily, he survived.

The most famous bushranger of all was Ned Kelly. He was captured in Djilamatang Nation after being tracked down by trackers from Wannamutta and Werannabe communities. Our history shows that the police took credit for the capture of Ned Kelly, but if it wasn't for the trackers, Kelly may never have been found. The trackers were promised payment for finding Kelly but they never received it. Next time you hear about Ned Kelly, remember that it was First Nations people who were responsible for his capture.

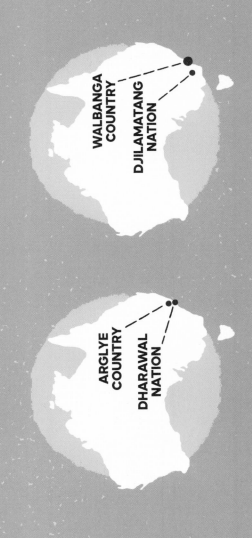

WALBANGA
COUNTRY

DJILAMATANG
NATION

ARGLYE
COUNTRY

DHARAWAL
NATION

WAR

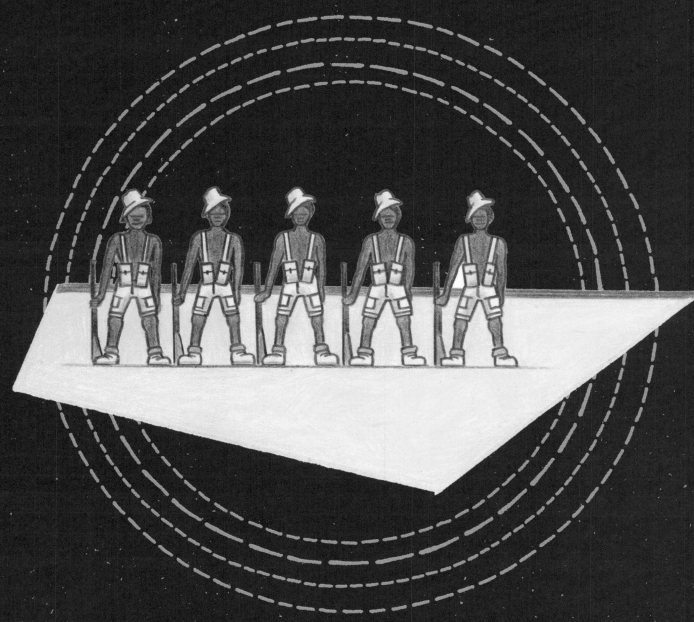

In the 1940s, during World War II, First Nations people were employed to patrol Australia's north, and search for Japanese submarines and ships that were trying to make surprise attacks. They kept a lookout and observed small changes to the ocean that they had grown up caring for, including looking for the shadows of submarines. They also looked out for Japanese soldiers parachuting to the land from aircraft, and made sure equipment was maintained and ready to use.

First Nations soldiers formed a wing of the Australian Army Reserve called Norforce but were nicknamed 'Nackeroos', probably for their ability, or 'nack', of picking up information. It's said that without the help of the Nackeroos and their scientific knowledge, the soldiers from the Australian Defence Force would've struggled with the tough uncompromising terrain. In spite of this, Norforce was only made official in 1981. It still exists today.

In May 1941, the Torres Strait Islands 51st Light Infantry Battalion was established by the Australian Defence Force because they were concerned about war escalating to the Pacific. The battalion was originally made up of 100 men and eventually grew to 830. In 1942, they supported the 14th garrison battalion to protect the Horn Island Airfield from the Japanese.

Still to this day, the Australian Defence Forces maintain a strong relationship with First Nations people across Australia, helping to form an understanding of Country and how it works.

MAPS

If you're travelling through Australia today and using a GPS map, chances are you have the first scientists to thank for developing it. Often the first scientists' knowledge, passed down from generation to generation, was translated into maps for safe passage through the bush.

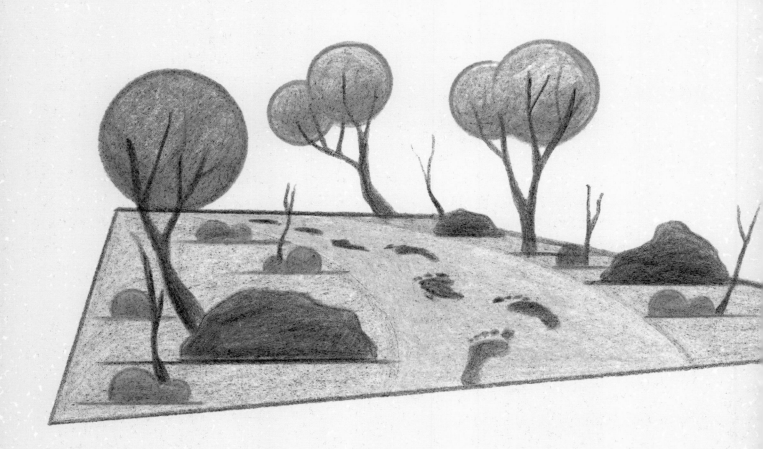

In 1791, the Eora people were hired to map the Hawkesbury River system in New South Wales. Then in the 1800s, the Dharawal people, along with the Gandangara and Darug peoples, had an important role in mapping the Blue Mountains of Sydney, New South Wales.

DHARAWAL, GANDANGARA & DARUG PEOPLES

TECHNOLOGY

ONE ARM POINT COMMUNITY

Today, First Nations people often work alongside modern-day scientists who are hoping to understand animals and the climate. Sometimes, despite having all the bells and whistles of modern technology, the old tried and tested methods of knowledge gained over thousands of years work better.

Scientists working to save the Australian bilby have enlisted ranger groups across Australia. The Birriliburu rangers are one of the groups that are helping track down bilbies in the desert. The Birriliburu rangers don't need fancy equipment or technology to find these animals. All their technology is in their head. They use lessons taught by their Elders, looking for subtle bilby prints (jina) in the sand and using knowledge of bilby behaviour that has been passed down over generations. This local knowledge is thousands of years old, whereas modern technology is only decades old.

The Bardi people from the north end of Dampier Peninsula in Western Australia have been using forensic science to track marine life for thousands of years. They look for small differences in the ocean floor or in the waves. For example, dugongs move slowly across the ocean floor as they eat

sea grass and this muddies up the water, creating tracks that lead the Bardi people straight to the dugongs.

Using the knowledge of our first scientists, First Nations rangers and modern-day scientists are now working together to track down sea turtles and protect them from overfishing and pollution. In one year (2020), Anindilyakwa Land and Sea Rangers cleaned up more than two tonnes of marine debris. This included discarded fishing nets (ghost nets), bottles, toothbrushes and cigarette lighters. All these items are made from plastic, and are washed onto the beaches of the Groote Archipelago from countries far away. The rangers are also managing breeding sites and protecting the turtles' eggs from being eaten by feral animals so that they will be around for future generations.

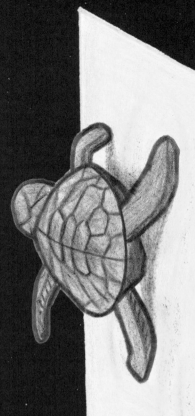

A NEW WORLD OF TECH

There are a number of deadly organisations run by First Nations people doing awesome things with science.

Indigitek is one example. It was founded in 2015, and empowers mob to pursue a career in STEM areas, with the expectation that 75 per cent of future jobs will be in STEM by 2025. Our people were the first scientists in Australia and traditional knowledge is still teaching us today. The need for more First Nations people in STEM has never been greater.

Another deadly program is Indigital, run by Dharug woman Mikaela Jade. Founded in 2014, Indigital is Australia's first Indigenous tech education company. It specialises in technology development, digital skills and even augmented reality! Their mission is to decrease the divide in education between Indigenous Australians and non-Indigenous Australians.

The last deadly tech organisation is Indigi Lab, founded by proud Kuku-Yalanki man Luke Briscoe. Briscoe is also a board member of DeadlyScience, supplying First Nations kids around the country with STEM resources. Indigi Lab runs hackathons where kids can pick up and learn new technologies and solve problems in real time. They focus on developing skills and a passion for tech. And they're so good at what they do, they've won awards, including the Indigenous Digital Excellence Award.

THE FIRST CHEMISTS

The first scientists never needed to go to the chemist. They created and produced their own incredible bush medicines by blending plants and animals to create remedies that treated illness and injuries. Some of these medicines are among the oldest in the world, and are still used today.

Maybe next time you're at the shops you can try to spot some of the first scientists' medicine.

SKINCARE

Kakadu plum (or billy goat plum), found all over northern Australia, is the world's richest natural source of vitamin C. One piece of fruit contains 100 times the vitamin C of an orange. Not surprisingly, today Kakadu plum is known as a superfood.

The first chemists have been using the Kakadu plum for thousands of years. Today, it is also crushed up into a creamy paste and applied to faces around the world to keep them pretty! There's no need to chase the latest cosmetic fad – we have our own deadly skincare right here in Australia!

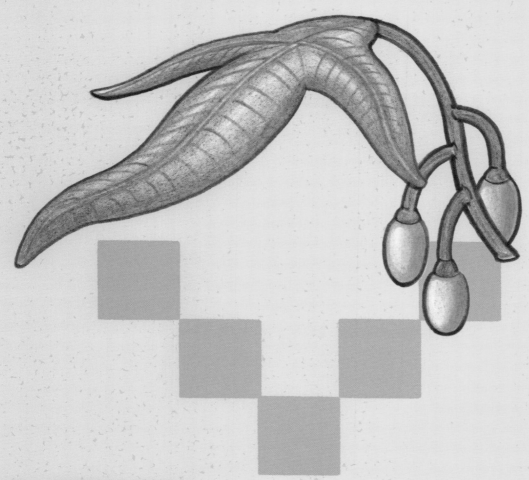

BUSH MEDICINE

The most famous bush medicine is tea-tree oil (bulam), which is made by crushing tea-tree leaves. It's a natural antiseptic and the Bundjalung people made it into a paste to treat wounds, or a tea to soothe a sore throat.

Today, tea-tree oil is used around the world to treat many different conditions, from acne to fungal infections. It is one of the world's oldest medicines, and the knowledge of how to use it has been passed down for thousands of years.

Kangaroo apple is another famous bush medicine. It grows in cooler climates and is found in Yuin, Ngunnawal and Kurnai Countries, and as far south as Pyemmairrener Country in northern Tasmania. The first chemists worked out that kangaroo apple is a natural steroid that, when ripe, makes an excellent treatment for cuts, burns, bruises and fractures. Kangaroo apple is also good bush tucker, and the ripe fruit was used for trading and eating.

The unripe kangaroo apple is poisonous, and when ground up it can be used to temporarily remove the oxygen from small bodies of water. This leaves the fish stunned and shocked, allowing people to easily grab a delicious feed. No need for fishing rods here! This was the original fish market.

Today, if you have a sore throat, chances are you'll be made better thanks to the medicine used by the first chemists. How so? Eucalypt leaves harvested by first scientists were boiled to produce oil. This was then used to make teas that helped overcome illness.

Eucalyptus oil is now used in cold and flu medications, like lozenges and cough syrups. So when you've been sick, you've probably had a product that uses the same eucalyptus oil that our first chemists used.

WOUND TREATMENT

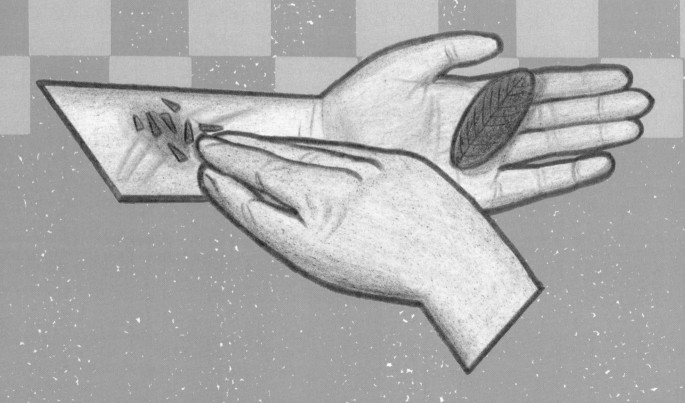

First scientists in Central Australia have used witchetty grubs ('maku' in Pitjantjatjara) as a food source. But they aren't just a tasty treat. The first scientists crushed up witchetty grubs and made them into a paste to heal the skin. The paste was applied to wounds and covered with a bandage or cloth made from dingo or kangaroo skin.

The Gumbaynggir people had another interesting way of treating wounds. First they started with the sap of the bloodwood tree and placed it on any cuts. The sap crystallised over the wound, stopping the bleeding. The sap was also antiseptic, so it killed all the bad bacteria that could cause infections.

After the sap was applied, goat's foot leaves were harvested, crushed and wrapped around the wound as a bandage. This promoted healing while also preventing infection. Goat's foot was also used for pain relief to help treat headaches and migraines, as well as nasty stings from stone fish and stingrays.

HEALTHY SUGARS

The community of Papunya is named after a Dreamtime story about the honey ant. These ants aren't like your regular ant, and have long been used by First Nations communities in the deserts of South Australia, Western Australia and the Northern Territory.

Honey ants live in complex tunnel systems of plants in the ground, and have a large ball of liquid sugar on their backs. They are delicious and taste sweet, but they also serve an important purpose.

In the desert, water can be tough to find. The hot, dry conditions can quickly make you dehydrated and there are long distances between bodies of water. As well as being a yummy treat, the honey ants kept the first scientists hydrated while they searched for water. Who would have thought ants could be delicious and good for you!

The honey ant is still eaten today, and is even used by some restaurants across Australia!

DESERT COMMUNITIES

BUSH SOAP

When travelling, the first scientists never needed to pack soap. All they needed was the red ash tree. When you crush and rub its leaves, it creates soap right in the palm of your hands. If mixed with water it creates a shampoo-like substance. This helped people from the nations across New South Wales and Queensland keep clean. Today, you can buy bush soap from most supermarkets.

The Utopia community use another bush soap called lywemp-lywemp to wash their hair and skin.

Today, this knowledge is shared with future scientists around the country in most botanical gardens.

ART
PRESERVATION

The first scientists were incredible artists who developed rock paints made from natural ochre and carefully selected barks. These paints were used to communicate stories and records of what was seen. They were like the first ever computer hard drive!

To this day, some of these paintings still exist tens of thousands of years later. How have they survived? Well, the first chemists had a trick to ensure the paintings lasted so that knowledge could be passed down. They collected eggs from birds and reptiles because egg yolks contain a natural glue. They mixed the yolk with the paint which then sealed it onto the surface, preserving it.

To put this into perspective, Leonardo da Vinci's *Mona Lisa*, one of the world's most famous paintings, is about 515 years old. It needs to be kept in a climate-controlled environment to make sure it survives, whereas the first chemists' paintings have lasted through all kinds of weather. Some paintings are over 40,000 years old!

These paintings also record species that no longer exist, like giant megafauna and Tasmanian tigers on the mainland of Australia. Even though those animals are no longer with us, we can thank the first scientists for showing us that they once were.

PROFESSOR LISA JACKSON PULVER AM

A proud Koori woman, Professor Lisa Jackson Pulver AM left home at 14, but this didn't stop her one bit. She had a love of learning and a burning desire to help others. So she began studying a bridging course which allowed her entry into university.

Jackson Pulver worked extremely hard and learnt as much as she could, graduating with a hospital-based – List A – Registered General Nursing certificate from the Schedule 5 Lidcombe Hospital. She worked as an intern at Lidcombe Hospital which gave her on-the-job training. In 1981, Jackson Pulver graduated from medicine at the University of Sydney.

Jackson Pulver had big ideas about what she wanted to do. She wanted to teach First Nations people about health, and help young kids who were unwell. She studied postgraduate epidemiology and, in 2003, was the first Aboriginal woman at the University of Sydney to become a doctor (PhD) of medicine. A few years later, she became a professor, which is one of the highest academic ranks at university. She then started to teach the next generation of young doctors, public health officials and medical professionals.

Not only is Jackson Pulver an incredible scientist, but she is also a group captain in the Royal Australian Air Force and Deputy Vice Chancellor of the University of Sydney, where she helps First Nations people study. She is also on the Board of the Australian Medical Council.

Professor Jackson Pulver is a modern-day deadly scientist who has proven that with a love of learning and a bit of belief, one day you can make a difference.

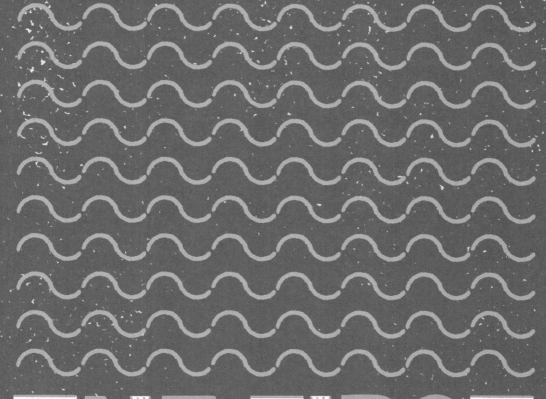

THE FIRST
LAND MANAGERS

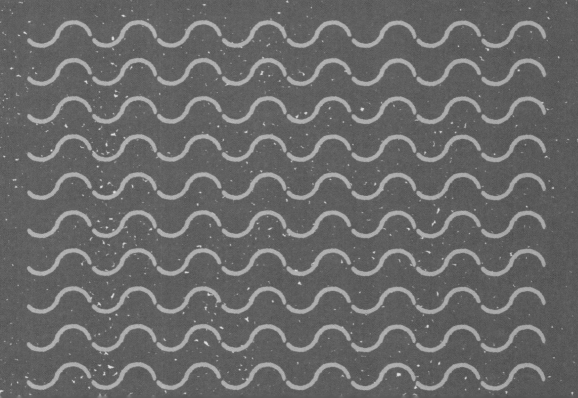

The first scientists had a deep belief that if you cared for Country, the Country would care for you. They practised land management techniques which were passed down from Elders, and adapted. Some of these techniques are still alive today, while others have been revived.

Caring for Country is not just a part of everyday life for First Nations peoples, it's part of our identity. For example, in the Wiradjuri Nation, some clans say that the water reeds are like the kidneys that keep the river system clean. The water cares for First Nations peoples and they work together to protect and care for Country.

In 2020, during the devastating bushfire season, important conversations were had about the first scientists and the way they managed the land. The importance of culture started to flower again.

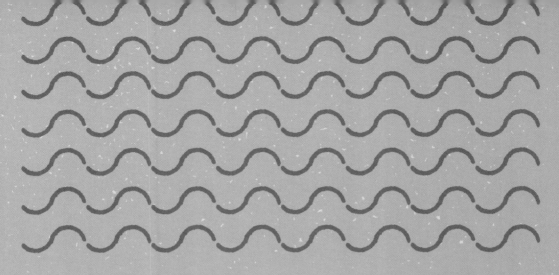

CREATING FOOD

The first scientists burnt parts of their Country to stop certain trees from taking hold. They knew that native grasses grew fast and wild, so fire was needed to control them. This protected the people and the land from devastating bushfires.

Burns were applied to very small areas which were connected to bushland or creeks. As new growth emerged, it created a new food source for the animals. This helped create a new generation of animals for the first land managers to use as a food source.

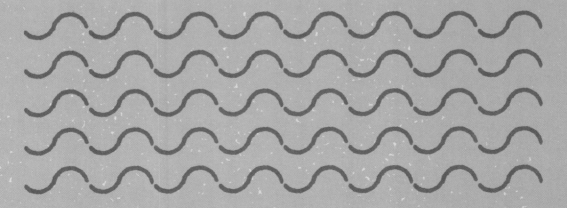

USING FIRE

For over 65,000 years, the first scientists carefully managed the land with fire.

Fire has been a part of storytelling and culture for many generations. It is used as a tool to promote healing of plants and trees.

The first scientists used cool burns to help regenerate the bush. This happened at different times of the day and night, depending on what type of Country was being burnt and in what season. Plants can be more flammable during the summer season because of the dry conditions.

During the day when it's hot, plants sweat out flammable oils, but during the night they produce dew. Burning at the right time when the plants are less flammable helps make the fire manageable.

The Miwatj people of Yolŋu Country look to the sky to know when it's time to burn. When the Pleiades constellation appears among the stars, it tells them that it's time to safely burn the land. In the desert it's the Seven Sisters' appearance in the sky that tells the Yolŋu people that it's time to burn.

First Nations fire management keeps the Country balanced by reducing the density of plants. This allows a greater variety of plants to grow and establish themselves. This in turn creates homes and food sources for many different animals.

YOLŊU COUNTRY

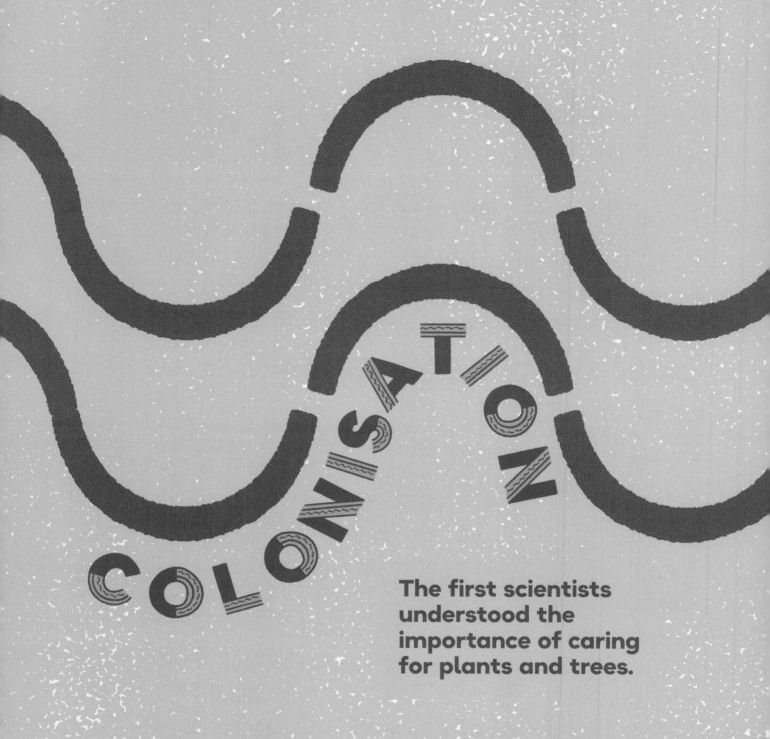

COLONISATION

The first scientists understood the importance of caring for plants and trees.

The first land managers burnt Country for the love of Country. After colonisation some of their methods were stopped in many areas. Without the ancient practices of cool burns and First Nations fire management, the land suffered. Instead out-of-control bushfires burnt high into the tops of trees – a sacred place for animals to escape the heat and fire.

Some wattle trees respond well to these hot fires. In fact, they respond too well. The fire makes the tree sweat and internal seed re-germinate, helping them spread and take up ground from other plants. This limits the range of food sources for small animals, and places to hide.

Since colonisation many animals have become extinct, or are currently threatened with extinction. And it's estimated that 100 plants have become extinct since colonisation. This can be directly linked to the lack of First Nations's fire management.

MODERN-DAY BURNS

Cultural burns developed by the first scientists are practised today. The First Nations people in Arnhem Land burn the land in patches, so that it can be easily controlled, to promote new growth. Absolute care and meticulous preparation is required to make sure these burns don't get out of control. They are normally done in the wet season, so that if a bushfire breaks out in the dry season, the fire doesn't have enough fuel to burn and scar the land.

Traditional burn practices have largely been ignored by governments. But since 2010, awareness has been building in New South Wales, and some cultural burning has been brought back to help with land management.

Unfortunately, in many areas of New South Wales and Victoria the land was previously burnt incorrectly and it was too late. In 2020, bushfires created havoc across Australia causing huge damage, in some areas beyond repair.

The year 2020 saw our most devastating bushfires, but bushfires have been contributing to extinction since colonisation.

Although the land has been damaged since colonisation, it's not too late to listen to our First Nations peoples and try to undo some of the damage. We need to help Country heal and recover, so that it can care for us.

LEADERS WITH A

Lille Madden

Lille Madden is a proud Arrernte, Bundjalung and Kalkadoon woman who grew up on Gadigal Country. She has a burning passion for the environment and all things animals. She started out as a bird keeper at Taronga Zoo and is now the Sydney coordinator for Seed Mob, the Indigenous Youth Climate Coalition that is spreading awareness about climate change from a First Nations perspective.

Madden also works for Jiwah, an Aboriginal-owned company that specialises in cultural landscape design. They have been doing some deadly work on Gadigal land at South Eveleigh, Sydney, creating and building cultural gardens in public spaces and on rooftops.

Paul Sinclair

Paul Sinclair is a proud Anaiwan man with a passion for spiders. Yes, spiders! When I was a young budding scientist I had a similar passion for all things creepy-crawly. It can be hard to be what you can't see, so meeting Sinclair changed my life. Back then, in 2007, Sinclair was a zookeeper at Sydney's Taronga Zoo, and he was very similar to me in many ways. When I said to him, 'I'm probably not smart enough to be a zookeeper' Sinclair responded by saying, 'Your greatest limitation is the one you place on yourself.' These wise words left a lasting impact.

Sinclair is now Director of a deadly company called Mirri Mirri that works to improve understanding and awareness of First Nations cultures. The company also helps young First Nations people find meaningful employment. I think Sinclair is deadly!

DEADLY PASSION

Aunty Rosie McGrady

Aunty Rosie is a proud Gamilaroi woman who founded an organisation called Culturally Informed Practices. She's fortunate to have cultural knowledge passed down to her by her Elders. She's passionate about education and empowering her community, as well as the wider Australian community.

Until the late 1960s, many young First Nations people were taken away from their families. This led to a lot of mobs losing some cultural identity. That's sad, because without culture you feel like something is missing. But Elders like Aunty Rosie are helping people find that connection to culture again, and heal from trauma.

Joe Williams

Joe Williams is a proud Wiradjuri/ Wolgalu man and founder of the Enemy Within project, which helps people who struggle with mental illness.

The former South Sydney Rabbitohs National Rugby League player made a lasting impact on my life after we met in 2018. Williams is all about passion and purpose, and the importance of being mentally well and connected with your culture.

Recently Williams was made an Adjunct Associate Professor at the School of Psychology, University of Queensland. He is deadly inspiring!

THE FIRST ECOLOGISTS

For First Nations people, the Dreamtime relates to the animals that have inhabited Australia for thousands of years. These animals relied on the first scientists to care for them and ensure their home was safe.

The first scientists had rules around hunting and fishing. They were very simple. You only took what you needed, and you released what you didn't need. This prevented the animals from dying out so that there was still food for future generations. Today more than ever, these rules are needed as the oceans are running out of fish and species are becoming extinct.

PLASTICS & CARBON EMISSIONS

Across Australia, descendants of the first scientists are waging a battle against plastic waste and climate change, which are both enemies of animals.

Seed Mob, an organisation of young First Nations people and scientists, is taking on the mess made by humans. They are standing strong to protect our environment by raising awareness about the impacts of climate change on First Nations people. They also campaign for governments and big business to reduce carbon emissions to help protect the oceans and our planet.

Turtles and other animals often mistake plastics for their natural food sources. This is a serious problem because these animals are unable to digest plastic and often become sick and die. Across the Torres Strait Islands, from Poruma Island, young deadly scientists have been collecting rubbish and litter to prevent it from going into the oceans. They are protecting animals for the next generation – this is modern-day caring for Country. Now that is crazy deadly!

PROTECTING

The knowledges of the first scientists are still used to protect and manage animals.

In Australia's north, First Nations rangers are often employed to track down troublesome crocodiles and remove them from waterways where they are a risk to humans. The population of saltwater crocodiles has grown as more humans have moved into their habitats. Luckily teams of rangers are able to move these naughty crocs to locations that are safer for both humans and crocs.

First Nations peoples are also playing an important role in protecting species on Groote Eylandt like the northern quoll, brush-tailed rabbit rat, masked owl and northern hopping mouse. They are keeping down feral cat populations which kill small animals like the quoll, and destroy the habitat.

Anindilyakwa Land and Sea Rangers track down these feral cats using infra-red technology and specialised trapping techniques, and then remove them. This means that species like the northern quoll are now thriving, while in other parts of Australia they are in decline.

First Nations peoples have also been combining traditional knowledges with new technologies to protect species in Kakadu National Park. Rangers and scientists from the CSIRO have been using drones alongside the knowledge of animal behaviour passed down from the first scientists. Together, they are tracking waterbird populations and working to protect them for years to come.

The Northern Australia Environmental Resources Hub also works with Traditional Owners to improve water quality and reduce pollution in places like Daly River in the Northern Territory. This has a direct impact on caring for the native animals. Often scientists collect water and soil samples to test for animal DNA, and this is then used by First Nations rangers to track which animals live where, and how to best manage feral populations. The combination of modern science and the knowledge passed on from generation to generation is a two-way approach which ensures greater protection of species.

Rangers are also using sensor cameras to track down Asian water buffalo and record how their numbers have grown. Water buffalo were introduced into northern Australia in the nineteenth century for food. When released, they became feral and populations are now estimated at up to 200,000.

Water buffalo may be cute but they have a taste for native grasses, and their hooves dig up and damage the land. This prevents new grasses from establishing themselves. So the data from the sensor cameras helps the rangers decide how many buffalo they need to hunt to keep them under control. Water buffalo have become a food source for many communities across the Northern Territory.

CANE
TOADS

FROG HOLLOW
COMMUNITY

In the Gija community a new generation of scientists are taking on the fight against cane toads.

Students from Purnululu Aboriginal Independent Community School are helping rangers and community members rid their Country of these pests.

The cane toad was first introduced into Queensland in 1935 to combat the cane beetle, but it was quickly found that cane toads failed to get the job done. Instead they destroyed populations of reptiles, birds and mammals. They have now migrated to the north coast of New South Wales, west into the Northern Territory, and into the Kimberley region in Western Australia, causing damage to the land.

In the wet season from January to March, a cane toad can produce 8,000–35,000 eggs at a time, sometimes twice a year. These eggs turn into tadpoles which compete for food with other native species. Just like the adult cane toads, tadpoles produce toxin that is lethal to most animals.

Deadly scientists from Purnululu have been venturing out on Country with their telescopes for astronomy evenings, but at the same time they collect cane toads, who like to travel at night to avoid the searing heat of the day.

These new deadly scientists have also worked with local rangers and Elders to develop plastic tadpole traps. They use bait to attract the tadpoles into the traps and then humanely destroy them. This is helping stop the cane toad in its tracks.

DISCOVERING
NEW ANIMALS

OLKOLA &
ANYARA COUNTRY

MARDOOWARRA
COUNTRY

Challenge yourself to see how you can help. You can be the change to save our wildlife.

First Nations peoples have not just been protecting existing species, they have also been discovering animals we previously didn't know about.

In 2019, researchers teamed up with local First Nations rangers in Uradi to conduct what is known as a 'bush blitz'. This is a huge search for different animals and plants.

During this particular search a new legless lizard called the Olkola slider skink (shown left) was discovered. However, this wasn't a new species for the Djagaraga or Gudang people. They had already fondly named the lizard Anyara, after their Country called Anyara. This Country is known as 'worm Country'.

First Nations peoples from the Mardoowarra region recently worked with scientists from the University of Melbourne and, during a 'water blitz', found an incredible 20 new species of fish in the mouth of the Mardoowarra (Fitzroy River).

The new fish were given traditional names by the local community members. Researchers took DNA samples of them to better study the fish, and will continue to work with the community to better understand and protect them.

Across the country, scientists and researchers are continuing to connect with First Nations scientists to help preserve and protect wildlife. But even more attention needs to be paid to First Nations perspectives and methods to create better protection plans for plants and wildlife.

A NEW GENERATION OF DEADLY SCIENTISTS

Deadly young scientists are doing cool things in classrooms around Australia.

In the Robinson River community, there is a small but very cool group of deadly young Garawa scientists doing all things STEM. From building water rockets to doing some deadly chemistry, they have been creating awesome videos that show their experiences of learning and discovery.

Deadly scientists from Aminjarrinja community on Groote Eylandt, who are at boarding school in Queensland, are a long way from home for most of the school year. But that hasn't stopped them spending their spare time learning science.

With resources provided by DeadlyScience, these young scientists are asking the kinds of questions natural scientists ask. For example, why does a blue-tongue lizard have a blue tongue? Well, in the animal kingdom anything the colour blue is generally venomous. However, blue-tongue lizards aren't venomous – they're the ultimate creature of bluff. They huff and they puff and they make themselves larger to ward off predators.

Another group of deadly young scientists is the mob from Manyallaluk School who have been using all types of incredible science blended with traditional knowledge. This includes using a microscope to look closely at spearheads, or setting up cameras to check out some cheeky water buffalo hanging about their school.

So what are you waiting for? Get out there and do some deadly science. Be inspired, be wowed, be amazed, but most importantly be deadly!

REFERENCES

The first astronomers

Cairns, H & Yidumduma Harney, B, 2003, *Dark Sparklers: Yidumduma's Wardaman Aboriginal Astronomy Night Skies Northern Australia*, HC Cairns, Merimbula.

Clarke, P, 2003, *Where the Ancestors Walked: Australia as an Aboriginal Landscape*, Allen & Unwin, Sydney.

Eseli, P, 1998, Eseli's Notebook, Aboriginal and Torres Strait Islander Studies Unit, University of Queensland.

Fuller, RS, Norris, RP & Trudgett, M, 2014, 'The astronomy of the Kamilaroi people and their neighbours' in *Australian Aboriginal Studies*, vol. 2014(2), pp. 3–27.

Green, D, Billy, J & Tapim, A, 2010, 'Indigenous Australians' knowledge of weather and climate' in *Climatic Change*, vol. 100, pp. 337–354.

Hamacher, DW, 2020, 'New coins celebrate Indigenous astronomy, the stars, and the dark spaces between them' in The Conversation, 14 September 2020.

Hamacher, DW, 2021, 'The Moon plays an important role in Indigenous culture and helped win a battle over sea rights' in The Conversation, 12 February 2021.

Hamacher, DW, Tapim, A, Passi, S & Barsa, J, 2018, "Dancing with the stars": Astronomy and music in the Torres Strait' in *Imagining Other Worlds: Explorations in Astronomy and Culture*, eds Campion, N & Impey, C, Sophia Centre Press, Lampeter, UK, pp. 151–161.

Hamacher, DW, Barsa, J, Passi, S & Tapim, A, 2019, 'Indigenous use of stellar scintillation to predict weather and seasonal change' in *Proceedings of the Royal Society of Victoria*, vol. 131, pp. 24–33.

Hamacher, DW, & Norris, RP, 2011, 'Eclipses in Australian Aboriginal Astronomy' in Journal of Astronomical History and Heritage, vol. 14(2), pp. 103–114.

Johnson, D, 1998, *Night Skies of Aboriginal Australia: A Noctuary*, Oceania Publications, Sydney.

Morieson, J, 1999, 'The Astronomy of the Boorong' in *Australian Journal of Indigenous Issues*, vol. 2(4), pp. 19–28.

Norris, R, 2016, 'Dawes Review 5: Australian Aboriginal astronomy and navigation' in *Publications of the Astronomical Society of the Pacific*, vol. 33, pp. 1–39.

Norris, RP & Hamacher, DW, 2009, 'The astronomy of Aboriginal Australia' in *The Role of Astronomy in Society and Culture Proceedings*, eds Valls-Gabaud, D & Boksenberg, A, Cambridge University Press, UK, pp. 39–47.

Norris, R & Norris, C, 2009, *Emu Dreaming: An Introduction to Australian aboriginal astronomy*, Emu Dreaming, Sydney.

Pascoe, B, 2014, *Dark Emu: Black Seeds: Agriculture or Accident?*, Magabala Books, Broome.

Personal communications from Yolŋu community members and senior educators at Yirrkala Bilingual school, 2020.

Stanbridge, WE, 1857, 'On the astronomy and mythology of the Aborigines of Victoria' in *Proceedings of the Philosophical Institute of Victoria*, vol. 2, pp. 137–140.

The first engineers

Boomerangs

Davidson, DS, 1936, 'Australian throwing sticks, throwing clubs and boomerangs' in *American Anthropologist*, vol. 38(1), pp. 76–100.

Gudem, P et al., 2020, 'flight dynamics of boomerangs: Impact of drag force and drag torque', AIAA Aviation Online Forum 2020, https://doi.org/10.2514/6.2020-2709

Vassberg, J, 2012, 'Boomerang flight dynamics', AIAA Applied Aerodynamics Conference, AIAA 2012, https://doi.org/10.2514/6.2012-2650

Fish traps

Gunditj Mirring Traditional Owners Aboriginal Corporation, n.d., https://www.gunditjmirring.com

Smith, A et al., 2019, 'Indigenous knowledge and resource management as World Heritage values: Budj Bim cultural landscape, Australia' in *Archaeologies,* vol. 15(2), pp. 285–313.

Fish and eel traps

Consultation with Elders from Brewarrina Aboriginal Cultural Museum, 2021.

Department of Agriculture, Water and the Environment, n.d., 'National heritage places: Brewarrina Aboriginal fish traps (Baiame's Ngunnhu)', https://www.environment.gov.au/heritage/places/national/brewarrina

Tan, M, 2015, 'The fish traps at Brewarrina are extraordinary ancient structures: Why aren't they better protected?' in *The Guardian*, https://www.theguardian.com/australia-news/2015/jul/10/fish-traps-brewarrina-extraordinary-ancient-structures-protection

Maclean, K et al., 2012, 'Ngemba water values and interests Ngemba Old Mission Billabong and Brewarrina Aboriginal fish traps (Baiame's Ngunnhu)', CSIRO, Australia, https://publications.csiro.au/rpr/pub?pid=csiro:EP127320

Shellfish traps

Attenbrow, V, 2018, 'Fishhooks, berá', Australian Museum, Discover & Learn, https://australian.museum/learn/cultures/atsi-collection/sydney/fishhooks-bera/

Attenbrow, V, 2010, 'Aboriginal fishing on Port Jackson, and the introduction of shell fish-hooks to coastal New South Wales, Australia' in *The Natural History of Sydney*, eds Hutching, P, Lunney, D & Hochuli, Royal Society of New South Wales, Mosman, pp. 16–34.

Glue

Australian Curriculum, n.d., 'Teacher background information', https://www.australiancurriculum.edu.au/TeacherBackgroundInfo?id=56600

Australian National Botanic Gardens Education Services, 2000, 'Aboriginal plant use and technology', https://www.anbg.gov.au/gardens/education/programs/pdfs/aboriginal_plant_use_and_technology.pdf

Ididjaustralia, 2014, 'Australian Aboriginal use of spinifex resin technology', https://www.youtube.com/watch?v=CoMKQww5pq8

Pitman, HT & Wallis, LA, 2012, 'The point of spinifex: Aboriginal uses of spinifex grasses in Australia' in *Ethnobotany Research and Applications*, vol. 10, pp. 109–131.

Renault, H, 2015, 'Researcher explores possibility of spinifex resin industry', ABC News, ABC Rural, QLD Country Hour, https://www.abc.net.au/news/rural/2015-04-07/australian-spinifex-resin-industry-exploration/6374148

Spearheads and arrowheads

Australian Museum, Discover & Learn, n.d., 2019, 'Kimberley spear points', https://australian.museum/learn/cultures/atsi-collection/cultural-objects/kimberley-spear-points/

Australian Museum, Discover & Learn, n.d., 2019, 'Prongs of a fishing spear', https://australian.museum/learn/cultures/atsi-collection/australian-archaeology/prongs-of-an-indigenous-fishing-spear-pre-1884/

Patten, JT, 2019, 'Spears: Form and function', Koori History, http://koorihistory.com/spears/

Nugent, S, 2015 'Sticks and stones: A functional analysis of Aboriginal spears from northern Australia', University of Queensland, https://doi.org/10.14264/uql.2015.403

Monroe, MH, 2013, 'Australia: The land where time began: A biography of the Australian continent: Aboriginal weapons and tools', https://austhrutime.com/weapons.htm

Reardon, A & Lauder, S, 2021, 'Repatriation of Gweagal spears from UK marked as "great win" for descendants', ABC News, ABC South East NSW, https://www.abc.net.au/news/2021-05-05/gweagal-spears-repatriated-from-united-kingdom/100117932?fbclid=IwAR3CtJmm79UMLeZJtSxfdzKMzN1uZwMkXkJOiKw7fjtRwqFmQBg4YdfmWWY

Ropes and handles

Australian National Botanic Gardens Education Services, 2004, 'Aboriginal plant use in south-east Australia', https://parksaustralia.gov.au/botanic-gardens/pub/aboriginal-plantuse.pdf

Gocher, K, 2009, 'Rare Indigenous rope making', ABC News, ABC Rural, https://www.abc.net.au/news/rural/2009-12-04/rare-indigenous-rope-making/6212458 (Sides, 2008)

Williams, A & Sides, T, 2008, *Wiradjuri Plant Use in the Murrumbidgee Catchment*, Murrumbidgee Catchment Management Authority, Wagga Wagga.

Canoes

Bickford, A, 1982, *People of the Murray River*, Methuen Australia, North Ryde.

Edwards, R, 1972, *Aboriginal Bark Canoes of the Murray Valley*, South Australian Museum, Rigby, Adelaide.

Payne, D, 2016, 'Gumung derrka and Na-riyarrku: Sewn bark canoes', Sea Museum, https://www.sea.museum/2016/12/15/australias-first-watercraft/canoes

Wheeler, H, 2019, 'Bark canoe from New South Wales', Australian Museum, Discover & Learn, https://australian.museum/learn/cultures/atsi-collection/cultural-objects/indigenous-bark-canoe-from-new-south-wales

Grinding stones

Aboriginal Victoria, n.d., 2021, 'Fact sheet: Aboriginal grinding stones', First Peoples – State Relations, State Government of Victoria, https://www.aboriginalvictoria.vic.gov.au/fact-sheet-aboriginal-grinding-stones

Fullagar, R et al., 2015, 'Evidence for Pleistocene seed grinding at Lake Mungo, south-eastern Australia' in *Archaeology in Oceania*, vol. 50(S1), pp. 3–19.

Bush ovens

Bickford, A, 1982, *People of the Murray River*, Methuen Australia, North Ryde.

Greenwood, P, 2014, 'Land of the Wiradjuri: Traditional Wiradjuri culture', https://visitlockhartshire.com.au/f.ashx/Traditional-Wiradjuri-Culture.pdf

Wright, W, 2006, 'Aboriginal cooking techniques', Australian National Botanic Gardens Education Services, https://www.anbg.gov.au/gardens/education/programs/pdfs/aboriginal-cooking-techniques-2006.pdf

David Unaipon

Jones, P, 1990, 'Unaipon, David (1872–1967)', Australian Dictionary of Biography, National Centre of Biography, Melbourne University Press, vol. 12, https://adb.anu.edu.au/biography/unaipon-david-8898

Coorong Country, n.d., 'David Unaipon', https://coorongcountry.com.au/david-unaipon/

Reserve Bank of Australia, n.d., 'David Unaipon (1872–1967)', https://banknotes.rba.gov.au/australias-banknotes/people-on-the-banknotes/david-unaipon/

Unaipon, D, 2001, *Legendary Tales of the Australian Aborigines*, eds Muecke, S & Shoemaker, A, Melbourne University Press, Carlton.

The first forensic scientists

Bush trackers

Brooke, B & Finch, A, 1999, 'Jane Duff's heroism: "The last great human bush story"?' in *The Latrobe Journal*, no. 63, http://www3.slv.vic.gov.au/latrobejournal/issue/latrobe-63/t1-g-t7.html

Clausen, L, 2014, 'Lost ones' in *The Monthly*, https://www.themonthly.com.au/issue/2014/december/1417352400/lisa-clausen/lost-ones#mtr

Webb, C, 2014, 'Story of young children's survival in Wimmera bush for nine days endures 150 years on' in *The Age*, https://www.theage.com.au/national/victoria/story-of-young-childrens-survival-in-wimmera-bush-for-nine-days-endures-150-years-on-20140810-101l2y.html

Bushrangers

Australian Government, Department of Communications, Information Technology and the Arts, Culture and Recreation Portal, 2008, 'Aboriginal trackers', https://web.archive.org/web/20080827232231/http://www.cultureandrecreation.gov.au/articles/indigenous/trackers/

Barker, B, 2007, 'Massacre, frontier conflict and Australian archaeology' in *Australian Archaeology*, vol. 64, pp. 9–14.

Brown, B, 2017, 'Re-enactment to look back at capture of Australia's deadliest bushrangers at Braidwood', ABC News, ABC South East NSW, https://www.abc.net.au/news/2017-04-10/anniversary-of-clarke-bushrangers-capture/8431500

Elder, B, 2003, *Blood on the Wattle: Massacres and Maltreatment of Aboriginal Australians since 1788*, 3rd edn, New Holland Press, Sydney.

Lowe, P, 2002, *Hunters and Trackers of the Australian Desert*, Rosenberg Publishing, Dural.

Maitland Mercury and Hunter River General Advertiser, 1880, 'The black trackers and the Kelly gang', https://trove.nla.gov.au/newspaper/article/810601

Reynolds, H, 1990, *With the White People: The Crucial Role of Aborigines in the Exploration and Development of Australia*, Penguin, Melbourne.

Richards, J, 1999, 'Moreton Telegraph Station: 1902 The Native Police on Cape York Peninsula', paper presented at the *History of Crime, Policing and Punishment Conference*, Australian Institute of Criminology, Canberra.

Richards, J, 2008, *The Secret War: A True History of Queensland's Native Police*, University of Queensland Press, St Lucia.

Sydney Morning Herald, 2000, 'Tracking down a just reward', https://www.smh.com.au/national/tracking-down-a-just-reward-20000330-gdfncv.html

War

Ball, R, 1996, *Torres Strait Force*, Australian Military History Publications, Loftus.

Dennis, P et al., 2008, *The Oxford Companion to Australian Military History*, 2nd edn, Oxford University Press, Melbourne.

Hall, RA, 1995, *Fighters from the Fringe : Aborigines and Torres Strait Islanders Recall the Second World War*, Aboriginal Studies Press, Canberra.

Hall, RA, 1997, *The Black Diggers: Aborigines and Torres Strait Islanders in the Second World War*, Aboriginal Studies Press, Canberra.

Tourism Northern Territory, n.d., 'Aboriginal history and war in the Top End', https://northernterritory.com/articles/aborigines-at-war

Vane, A, 2000, *North Australia Observer Unit: The History of a Surveillance Regiment*, Australian Military History Publications, Loftus.

Maps

Taçon, PSC et al., 2007, *Assessment of the Aboriginal Cultural Heritage Values of the Greater Blue Mountains World Heritage Area: A Report for the Department of Environment and Water Resources*, Blue Mountains World Heritage Institute's Natural and Cultural Heritage Program, https://static1.squarespace.com/static/59d6cf25be42d6c4c599565d/t/5a448d1671c10b32751c1142/1514442052238/Assessment+of+Aboriginal+Cultural+Heritage+Values.pdf

Technology

Burrows, N, Dunlop, J & Burrows, S, 2012, 'Searching for signs of bilby (*Macrotis lagotis*) activity in central Western Australia using observers on horseback' in *Journal of the Royal Society of Western Australia*, vol. 95, pp. 167–170.

Bush Heritage Australia, n.d., 'Bilbies', https://www.bushheritage.org.au/species/bilby

Dziminski, MA & Carpenter, F, 2016, 'The conservation and management of the bilby (*Macrotis lagotis*) in the Pilbara: Progress report 2016', Department of Parks and Wildlife, Perth.

Fleming, PA et al., 2013, 'Is the loss of Australian digging mammals contributing to a deterioration in ecosystem function?' in *Mammal Review*, vol. 44(2), pp. 94–108.

Jones, A, 2019, 'To save the bilby, these Traditional Owners and scientists have to work together', ABC News, ABC Science, https://www.abc.net.au/news/science/2019-04-07/bilby-conservation-indigenous-two-way-science/10966552

Lambert, K et al., 2014, 'Satellite tracking of hawksbill turtles on Groote Eylandt' in *Proceedings of the Second Australian and Second Western Australian Marine Turtle Symposia*, Perth, https://library.dbca.wa.gov.au/static/FullTextFiles/026652.005.pdf

McRae, M, 2017, 'Counting "cows of the sea" in the Kimberley' in *Ecos*, vol. 233, https://ecos.csiro.au/counting-cows-sea-kimberley/

Moodie, C, 2009, 'Aboriginal hunters adapt skills to scientific research and dugong conservation', ABC Local, https://www.abc.net.au/local/videos/2009/09/15/2686219.htm?site=local

Paltridge, R, 2016, 'What did we learn from the 2016 Ninu Festival?', Save the Bilby Fund, unpublished report.

Pavey, C, 2006, 'National recovery plan for the greater bilby *Macrotis lagotis*', Northern Territory Department of Natural Resources, Environment and the Arts.

Moseby, KE & O'Donnell, E, 2003, 'Reintroduction of the greater bilby, *Macrotis lagotis* (Reid) (*Marsupialia: Thylacomyidae*), to northern South Australia: Survival, ecology and notes on reintroduction protocols' in *Wildlife Research*, vol. 30, pp. 15–27.

Woinarski, JCZ, Burbidge, AA & Harrison, PL, 2015, 'Ongoing unraveling of a continental fauna: Decline and extinction of Australian mammals since European settlement' in *Proceedings of the National Academy of Sciences USA*, vol. 112(15), pp. 4531–4540.

Woinarski, JCZ, AA, & Harrison, PL, 2015, 'A review of the conservation status of Australian mammals' in *Therya*, vol. 6(1), pp. 155–166.

The first chemists

Cosmetics

Gorman, JT, Brady, C & Clancy, TF, 2019, *Management Program for* Terminalia ferdinandiana *in the Northern Territory of Australia 2019–2023*, Northern Territory Department of Environment and Natural Resources, Darwin.

Gorman, J et al., 2019, 'Kakadu plum (*Terminalia ferdinandiana*) as a sustainable Indigenous agribusiness' in *Economic Botany*, vol. 74(2), pp. 1–18.

Bush medicine

Consultation with Uncle Warren Forester from Yuin Country and Uncle Jiemba Daly, 2020.

Critchley, C, 2018, 'The endurance of bush medicine' in *Pursuit*, University of Melbourne, https://pursuit.unimelb. edu.au/articles/the-endurance-of-bush-medicine

Cromb, N, 2017, '10 bush medicines that have been curing people for generations', NITV, https://www.sbs.com. au/nitv/article/2017/05/25/10-bush-medicines-have-been-curing-people-generations

Hall, I, 2020, 'Aboriginal bush medicine: Uses of kangaroo apple' in *Imperial Bioscience Review*, https://imperialbiosciencereview.com/2020/10/02/aboriginal-bush-medicine-uses-of-kangaroo-apple/

Healy, J & University of Melbourne, 2018, *The Art of Healing: Australian Indigenous Bush Medicine*, Medical History Museum, Faculty of Medicine, Dentistry and Health Sciences, University of Melbourne, Parkville.

Issacs, J, 2002, *Bush Food: Aboriginal Food and Herbal Medicine*, New Holland Publishers, Frenchs Forest.

Jones, G, 2014, 'Indigenous medicine: A fusion of ritual and remedy' in *The Conversation*, https://theconversation.com/indigenous-medicine-a-fusion-of-ritual-and-remedy-33142

Kamenev, M, 2011, 'Top 10 Aboriginal bush medicines' in *Australian Geographic*, https://www.australiangeographic.com.au/topics/history-culture/2011/02/top-10-aboriginal-bush-medicines/

Locher, C, Semple, SJ & Simpson, BS, 2013, 'Traditional Australian Aboriginal medicinal plants: An untapped resource for novel therapeutic compounds?' in *Future Medicinal Chemistry*, vol. 5(7), pp. 733–736.

Packer, J et al., 2019, 'Building partnerships for linking biomedical science with traditional knowledge of customary medicines: A case study with two Australian Indigenous communities' in *Journal of Ethnobiology and Ethnomedicine*, vol. 15, p. 69.

Phillips, N, 2020, 'Traditional medicine, Aboriginal health and big pharma', Aboriginal Art UK, https://www.aboriginalartuk.com/post/long-read-traditional-medicine-aboriginal-health-big-pharma

Australian Tea Tree Industry Association, 2015, 'About Australian tea tree oil', https://teatree.org.au/teatree_about.php

Williams, CJ, 2020, *Bush Remedies*, Rosenberg Publishing, Dural.

Wound treatment

Arrawarra, 2009, 'Project fact sheets', Arrawarra Sharing Culture, http://www.arrawarraculture.com.au/fact_sheets/pdfs/00_Fact_Sheets_Booklet.pdf

Australian Aboriginal Bushfood and Medicines, 2020, https://vimeo.com/123054737?fbclid=IwAR3Z4Egxb-ug3 Le9hUy87OYzJwCLuG54LZz7z_0PlKx-76767x8xnbB1a1Q

Healthy sugars

Bourget, A, 2018, 'These sweet Australian ants are "the best honey you've ever tasted", SBS, https://www.sbs.com.au/food/article/2018/09/06/these-sweet-australian-ants-are-best-honey-youve-ever-tasted

Conway, JR, 1991, 'The biology and Aboriginal use of the honeypot ant, *Camponotus inflatus* Lubbock, in Northern Territory, Australia' in *The Australian Entomologist*, vol. 18(2), pp. 49–56.

Karlangu Aboriginal Art Centre, n.d., 'Bush plum Dreaming', https://www.karlangu.com/stories/31-bush-plum-dreaming

Morris, N, 2016, 'Honey ant hunters and Aboriginal culture keepers head bush to revive their language', ABC News, ABC Goldfields, https://www.abc.net.au/news/2016-06-16/honey-ant-hunters-and-aboriginal-culture-keepers-head-bush/7514170

Bush soap

Batchelor, NT, 2008, '*Inten-antey anem = "these things will always be": Films from the Utopia Bush Medicine Project 2007–2008*', Batchelor Institute of Indigenous Tertiary Education.

Cribb, AB & Cribb, JW, 1988, *Wild medicine in Australia*, Collins, Sydney.

Dengarden, 2019, 'Australian native plant profile: Soap tree (*Alphitonia Excelsa*)', https://dengarden.com/gardening/Soap-Tree-Alphitonia-excelsa-Red-Ash

Williams, CJ, 2012, *Medicinal Plants in Australia, Volume 3: Plants, Potions and Poisons*, Rosenberg Publishing, Dural.

Art preservation

Artlandish Aboriginal Art, 2018, 'Ochre Aboriginal art of the East Kimberley', Artlandish Aboriginal Art Gallery, Kununurra, https://www.aboriginalartshop.com/ochre-aboriginal-art/

Collins, B, 2019, 'It survived ice-ages and the rise and fall of oceans: How has Indigenous rock art lasted so long?', ABC News, ABC Kimberley, https://www.abc.net.au/news/2019-07-26/how-rock-art-lasts-thousands-of-years/11274940

Gondawananet, n.d., 'Aboriginal art history', http://www.gondwananet.com/aboriginal-art-history.html

The first land managers

Consultation with Victor Steffensen, 2021.

Chenery, S & Cheshire, B, 2020, 'Fighting fire with fire', ABC News, *Australian Story*, https://www.abc.net.au/news/2020-04-13/how-victor-steffensen-is-fighting-fire-with-fire/11866478?nw=0

Cook, GD, Jackson, S, & Williams, RJ, 2012, 'A revolution in northern Australia fire management: Recognition of Indigenous knowledge, practice and management' in *Flammable Australia: Fire Regimes, Biodiversity and Ecosystems in a Changing World*, eds Bradstock, RA, Gill, AM & Williams, RJ, CSIRO, Melbourne.

Ellis, EC et al., 2021, 'People have shaped most of terrestrial nature for at least 12,000 years' in *Proceedings of the National Academy of Sciences*, vol. 118(17), pp. 7 e2023483118.

Fletcher, MS, 2020, 'Our Country, our way', *Pursuit*, University of Melbourne, https://pursuit.unimelb.edu.au/articles/our-country-our-way

Fletcher, MS, Hall, T & Alexandra, AN, 2020, 'The loss of an Indigenous constructed landscape following British invasion of Australia: An insight into the deep human imprint on the Australian landscape' in *Ambio*, vol. 50(1), pp. 138-149.

Higgins, I, 2020 'Indigenous fire practices have been used to quell bushfires for thousands of years, experts say', ABC News, https://www.abc.net.au/news/2020-01-09/indigenous-cultural-fire-burning-method-has-benefits-experts-say/11853096

Kelly, LT & Brotons, L, 2017, 'Using fire to promote biodiversity' in *Science*, vol. 355(6331), pp. 1264–1265.

Korff, J, 2021, 'Aboriginal land management and care', Creative Spirits, https://www.creativespirits.info/aboriginalculture/land/aboriginal-land-care

Korff, J, 2021, 'Cool burns: Key to Aboriginal fire management', Creative Spirits, https://www.creativespirits.info/aboriginalculture/land/aboriginal-fire-management

Russell-Smith, J et al, 2013, 'Managing fire regimes in north Australian savannas: Applying Aboriginal approaches to contemporary global problems' in *Frontiers in Ecology and the Environment*, vol. 11, e55–e63.

Steffensen, V, 2020, *Fire Country: How Indigenous Fire Management Could Help Save Australia*, Hardie Grant Travel.

Yibarbuk, D, et al, 2001, 'Fire ecology and Aboriginal land management in central Arnhem Land, northern Australia: A tradition of ecosystem management' in *Journal of Biogeography*, 28(3), 325–44.

The first ecologists

Plastics and carbon emissions

Consultation with Gaye McKay, head of the recycling program on Poruma Island, 2020 and 2021.

Consultation with Lille Madden, Seed Mob, 2021.

Protecting animals

Anindilyakwa Land Council, 2021, 'Indigenous protected area', https://anindilyakwa.com.au/land-and-sea/indigenous-protected-area/

Bird, RB, Nyalangka, T, Codding, BF & Bird, DW, 2013, 'Niche construction and Dreaming logic: Aboriginal patch mosaic burning and varanid lizards (*Varanus gouldii*) in Australia' in *Proceedings of the Royal Society B*, vol. 280, 20132297.

Corey, B et al., 2017, 'Commercial harvests of saltwater crocodile *Crocodylus porosus* eggs by Indigenous people in northern Australia: Lessons for long-term viability and management' in *Oryx*, 52(4), pp. 697–708.

Gibb, K, 2019, 'Developing EDNA methods to detect Top End animals', Northern Australia Environmental Resources Hub, National Environmental Science Programme, https://www.nespnorthern.edu.au/wp-content/uploads/2019/11/Developing-eDNA-methods-to-detect-Top-End-animals-project-update.pdf

Gillespie, GR et al., 2015, 'A guide for the use of remote cameras for wildlife survey in northern Australia', Charles Darwin University, Darwin.

Heiniger, J et al., 2020, 'Demography and spatial requirements of the endangered northern quoll on Groote Eylandt' in *Wildlife Research*, vol. 47(3), pp. 224–238.

National Indigenous Australians Agency, n.d., 'Anindilyakwa IPA and rangers', https://www.niaa.gov.au/anindilyakwa-ipa-and-rangers

Cane toads

FrogId Team, 2021, 'Cane toad', Australian Museum, Discover & Learn, https://australian.museum/learn/animals/frogs/cane-toad/?gclid=CjwKCAiAm-2BBhANEiwAe7eyFGq7-gn4TGhe-87MJjfl3t97CvckB0zRLPnzULFlRGq_08z1wjYPoxoCaVwQAvD_BwE

Consultation with Purnululu Aboriginal Independent Community School and the community members, 2020.

Discovering new animals

Amey, AP, Couper, PJ & Worthington Wilmer, J, 2019, 'A new species of *Lerista* Bell, 1833 (*Reptilia: Scincidae*) from Cape York Peninsula, Queensland, belonging to the *Lerista allanae* clade but strongly disjunct from other members of the clade' in *Zootaxa*, vol. 463(1), pp. 161–171.

ACKNOWLEDGEMENTS

Anangu Pitjantjatjara Yankunytjatjara
Anindilyakwa Land Council
Anindilyakwa rangers
Arrandra Aunties
Associate Professor Duane Hamacher
Aunty Rosie McGrady
Aunty Ali Golding
Aunty Beryl Van-Oploo
Aunty Devone Anderson
Aunty Fleur Dennis
Aunty Isobel Reid
Aunty Josie Rose
Aunty Laura McBride
Aunty Lorraine Hatton
Aunty Sally Bower
Bianca Monaghan
Brewarrina Aboriginal Corporation
Charisma Cubillo
Chris Errington
Craig (Winna) Oldroyd
Djarindjin Aboriginal Corporation
Dorothy Yunipingu
Dr Jessica Rogers
Dr Mariko Smith
Dr Terri Janke
Ezekiel Kwaymullina
First people of the Millewa-Mallee
  Aboriginal Corporation
FISH (Foundation for Indigenous
  Sustainable Health)
Frog Hollow community
Groote Eylandt community
Irma Gold
Jasmine Williams
Jaynaya Winmar
Joe Sambono
Joe Williams

Karlie Noon
Kelly Gudgeon
Lillie Madden
Manyallaluk Community School
Mark Anderson
Merryn Curley
Michaela Skuthorpe
Miss Shalailah Carter
Molly Hunt
Paul Sinclair
Professor Bradley Moggridge
Professor Lisa Jackson Pulver
Professor Marcia Langton
Purnululu Aboriginal Independent
  Community School
Rachel Hocking
Richard Fejo
Robinson River School
Sam Osborne
Scott Ryan
Talah Laurie
Talei Eli
Thomas Mayor
Uncle Bruce Pascoe
Uncle Djalu Gurruwiwi
Uncle Feli McHughes
Uncle Jimmy Fejo
Uncle Kym Kropinyeri
Uncle Ray Splinter
Uncle Victor Steffensen
Uncle Warren Foster
Wunyungar Djadji
Wurundjeri Woi Wurrung Cultural
  Heritage Aboriginal Corporation,
  Heritage unit Elders
Yanti Ropeyarn
Yirrkala Bilingual School